Leap, Hare, Leap!

Dom Conlon
Illustrations Anastasia Izlesou

GRAFFEG

Leap, Hare, Leap!
Published in Great Britain in 2020 by Graffeg Limited.

Written by Dom Conlon copyright © 2020.
Illustrated by Anastasia Izlesou copyright © 2020.
Designed and produced by Graffeg copyright © 2020.

Graffeg, 24 Stradey Park Business Centre,
Mwrwg Road, Llangennech, Llanelli,
Carmarthenshire, SA14 8YP, Wales, UK.
Tel: 01554 824000. www.graffeg.com.

Dom Conlon is hereby identified as the author of this
work in accordance with section 77 of the Copyrights,
Designs and Patents Act 1988.

A CIP Catalogue record for this book is available from the
British Library.

ISBN 9781913134921

1 2 3 4 5 6 7 8 9

Leap, Hare, Leap!

Dom Conlon
Illustrations Anastasia Izlesou

This book belongs to:

_____

_____

_____

Dip-dwelling grass-grazer,
beautiful Hare – ask why she's standing,
ask what she hears.

Wait. Listen!

The field grass hisses and Hare's long
ears rise like hands in class.

She spies a flash of sunrise, a tail tipped
with cloud and...

...quick as a sniff, she's a firm-footed lea-leaper.
Leap, Hare, LEAP!

Leap into the sky. Let the world turn.
Where does Hare land?
In an American desert,
where the sun looks for
water in the earth's dry bowl
and where a jackrabbit bobs by.

Rabbit by name but hare through and through, Jackrabbit is a black-tailed scrub-scrambler who just wants to play.

Wait. Listen!

The crying coyote howls hunger in the air, so our Hare cannot stay here...

Leap, Hare, LEAP!

Leap to where the Arctic hare lives,
a mittened fist on snowy slopes.

Where is the Arctic hare? There!
Peeping from a fur-warm hole.
Could our Hare, our fire-eyed
moon-jumper, be safe with him?

15

No! Out of the dark sky – a ghost-swooper,

a stealthy hare-stalker, a snowy owl has seen them.

Stay out of sight, frost-furred friend.
Dip down in your hole and hide.

Leap, Hare, LEAP!

Leap to where the Woolly hare
lives, as shy as a shadow at noon.

Our wisp-whiskered dawn-dancer
blinks once, blinks twice.

There's grass on the land
and plants under trees,
but something is growling
through iron-set teeth...

Clinking and clanking in the woodlands
of China, a mechanical monster chews and
chomps through Woolly hare's home.
Get out of the way!

Leap, Hare, LEAP!

22

She leaps just in time and lands in Japan.

Now Hare is a meadow-otter, swimming through grass to a sun-soaked village.

Bark-biter, street-scurrier, the Japanese hare will lead her to safety, small though he is.

Then, with ink-dipped ears, the Japanese hare detects the tap, tap, tap of stealthy steps.

Hare looks. She's seen this before.

Back in the form where her leverets lie.

Has Fox followed her across the world?

Leap, Hare, LEAP!

She's back on the grass where her journey began.

And so is Fox. He's a splash of umber on the muddy field and he starts the chase.

Over the fields and through the wheat, Hare is a lithe-limbed hill-hopper carrying the sun on her back.

She must run or be caught, so...

Run, Hare, RUN!

She's a zig-zag-zoomer with lightning under her tail. She can escape.

Leap, Hare, LEAP!

Hare leaps to the farmhouse and Fox falls back.
They are watched by an amber-eyed child.

Hare waits until the coast is clear and then finds
her form once more.

Safe. Home. And... sleep, Hare, sleep!

Hare Facts

There are lots of different types, or species, of hare. The hare in our story is a European hare. She's often called a brown hare too, because her coat is mostly brown. She has long ears and a white belly and a white patch under her tail. This sort of hare lives in Europe and parts of the United Kingdom.

Most hares can run very fast – up to 60kph. That's faster than a fox, which can run up to 50kph. Usain Bolt, the fastest man in the world, managed to run 44kph.

Hares can leap really high too – up to 3m. The highest a human has ever jumped is 2.4m. Both of these are impressive, but a flea can leap 150 times its height - that's like leaping 250m.

The 'dip' in which hares live is called a form or scrape. Unlike rabbits, most hares don't burrow.

A baby hare is called a leveret. They are born with fur and the ability to run, which means they don't need the protection of a burrow. Leverets are born with their eyes open.

There are a few words in *Leap, Hare, Leap!* that you might not have heard before. These words are new, but not difficult.

Form – a shallow dip in the land
Lea – a bit of grassy land
Scrub – an area with wild bushes
Umber – a red-brown colour

Of course, our brave hare meets other hares on her journey. Here is some information about them.

The Hare Preservation Trust

Hares are different to rabbits – and once you see one, you will understand why. The brown hares are bigger and faster and have a very different way about them. There is a wonderful society helping educate people about hares – it's called the Hare Preservation Trust.

Some people still see hares as a nuisance. Thankfully, the Hare Preservation Trust does very important work to keep them safe.

www.hare-preservation-trust.co.uk

Black-tailed jackrabbit

Despite having the word 'rabbit' in its name, the jackrabbit is actually a hare. It can be found mostly in the American deserts, which means it is used to the heat. Fun fact on names: there's a rabbit called the Belgian Hare.

Woolly hare

The Woolly hare is found in China (there are quite a few different types of Chinese hare), India and Nepal. It is very shy and most awake at night (we call this 'nocturnal'). Other hares are more active early in the morning and in the evening (we call this 'crepuscular').

Arctic hare

The Arctic hare can be found in a few northern lands such as Greenland and some Arctic islands. In the very coldest places an Arctic hare's fur remains white. In other places its white fur will change to grey or brown during the summer.

Like most hares, they usually live on grasses and plants but have been known to eat fish, but unlike most hares, Arctic hares live in burrows.

Japanese hare

The Japanese hare can live in forests, where it is seen as a bit of a pest because it strips the bark from trees with its teeth. It can also live in rural areas such as villages. It's a reddish brown colour.

Dom Conlon

Dom Conlon is a poet, and whether talking on BBC Radio Lancashire or running workshops for children, Dom's work is guided by nature and the stars.

Nicola Davies said *Astro Poetica* was 'insightful, thought-provoking and fun', whilst Chris Riddell said *This Rock That Rock* contained 'words and pictures that are quite simply out of this world'. Dom hopes to inspire everyone to read and write poetry.

Anastasia Izlesou

Anastasia Izlesou is a multidisciplinary illustrator and designer from the UK. Using a mix of digital and traditional media, she creates vibrant work full of bold natural elements.

Her inspirations range from natural sciences, literature and folklore to everyday items and objects of kitsch.

The White Hare, published by Graffeg, was Anastasia's first published book.